Mega Multiplication MAZES

Angelika Scudamore

ARCTURUS

This edition published in 2020 by Arcturus Publishing Limited
26/27 Bickels Yard, 151–153 Bermondsey Street,
London SE1 3HA

Illustrated by Angelika Scudamore
Written by Catherine Casey
Designed by Trudi Webb
Edited by Sebastian Rydberg

ISBN: 978-1-83857-142-9
CH007815NT
pplier 33, Date 0820, Print run 10739

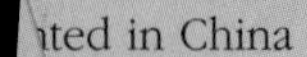
ted in China

How to Use This Book

Welcome to the "funtastic" world of mega multiplication mazes! This activity book is full of exciting scenes to help you learn and become confident with the basics of multiplication.

Locate the start of each maze, and read the instructions to help you solve it.

Solve each calculation, and then choose the correct path to reach the end.

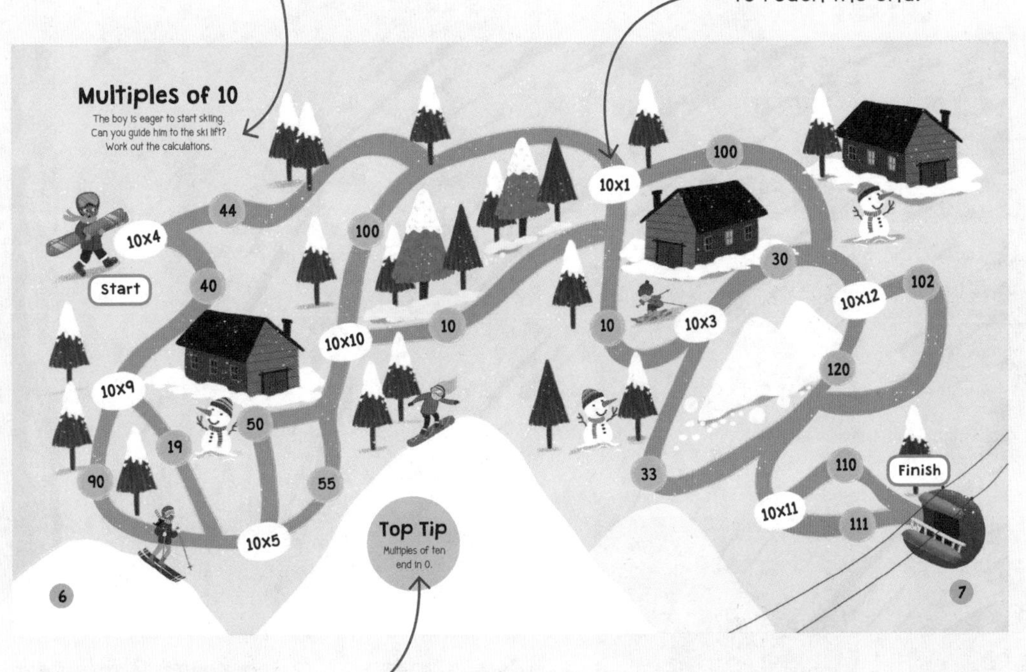

Some topics come with a Top Tip to help you on the way.

After you have completed the maze, check that you followed the correct route by turning to pages 30-32.

Multiples of 2

Lead the astronaut through the stardust back to the rocket. Follow the numbers that are multiples of 2.

Top Tip

Multiples of 2 are numbers in the two times table. Multiples of 2 can be divided by 2.

20
17
5
1
10
22
4
3
18
6
25
14
13
Finish

Multiples of 10

The boy is eager to start skiing.
Can you guide him to the ski lift?
Work out the calculations.

Top Tip

Multiples of ten end in 0.

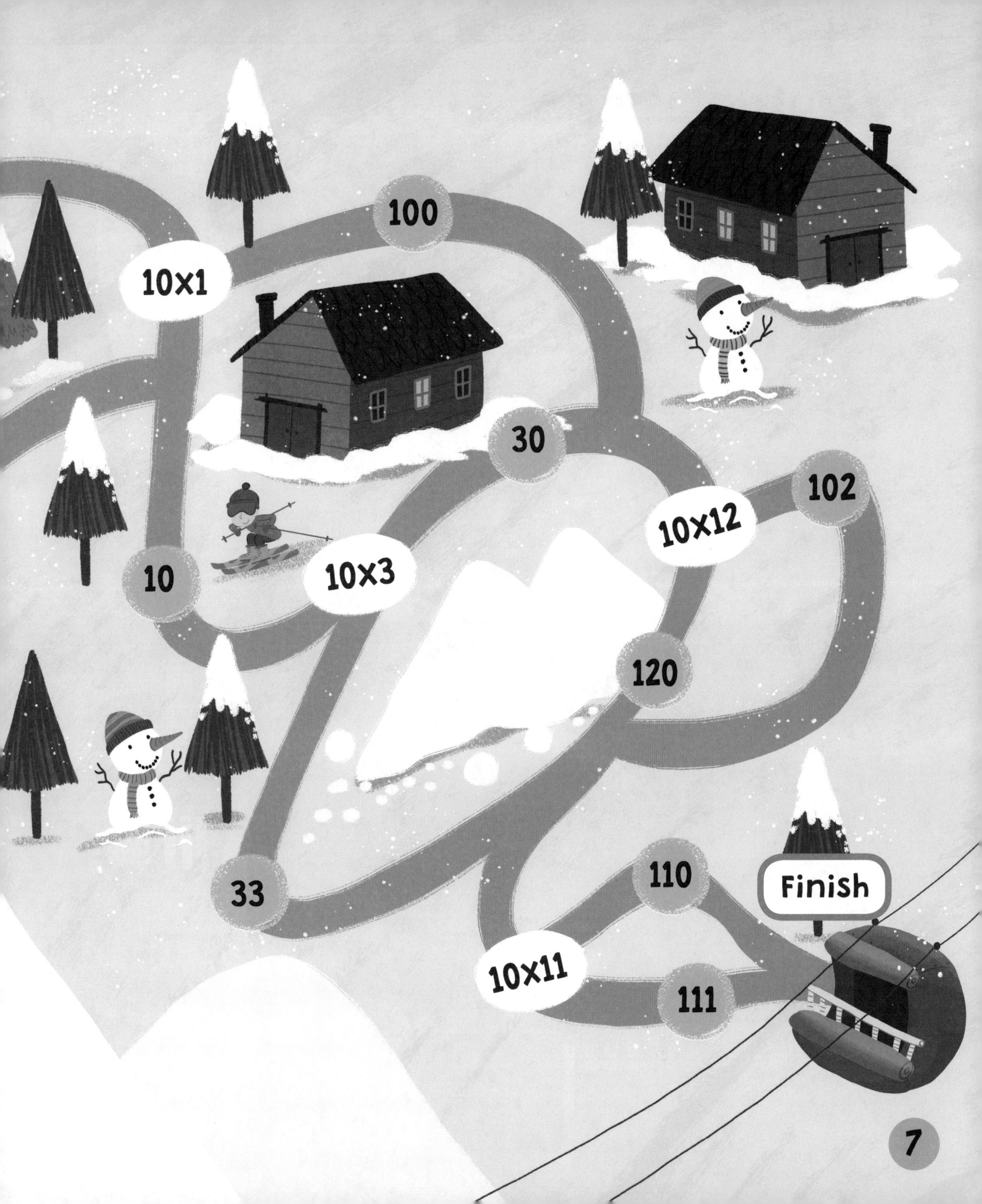
100
10x1
30
102
10x12
10
10x3
120
110
Finish
33
10x11
111

Multiples of 5

Lead the camel across the desert.
Follow the numbers that are multiples of 5.

Top Tip

Multiples of 5 end in 0 or 5.

59
10
5
Finish
25
15
28
50
36
35
19
54

Mixed multiples of 2, 5, and 10

Can you show the girl to the music room in time for her music lesson? Solve the multiplication problems and follow the correct answers.

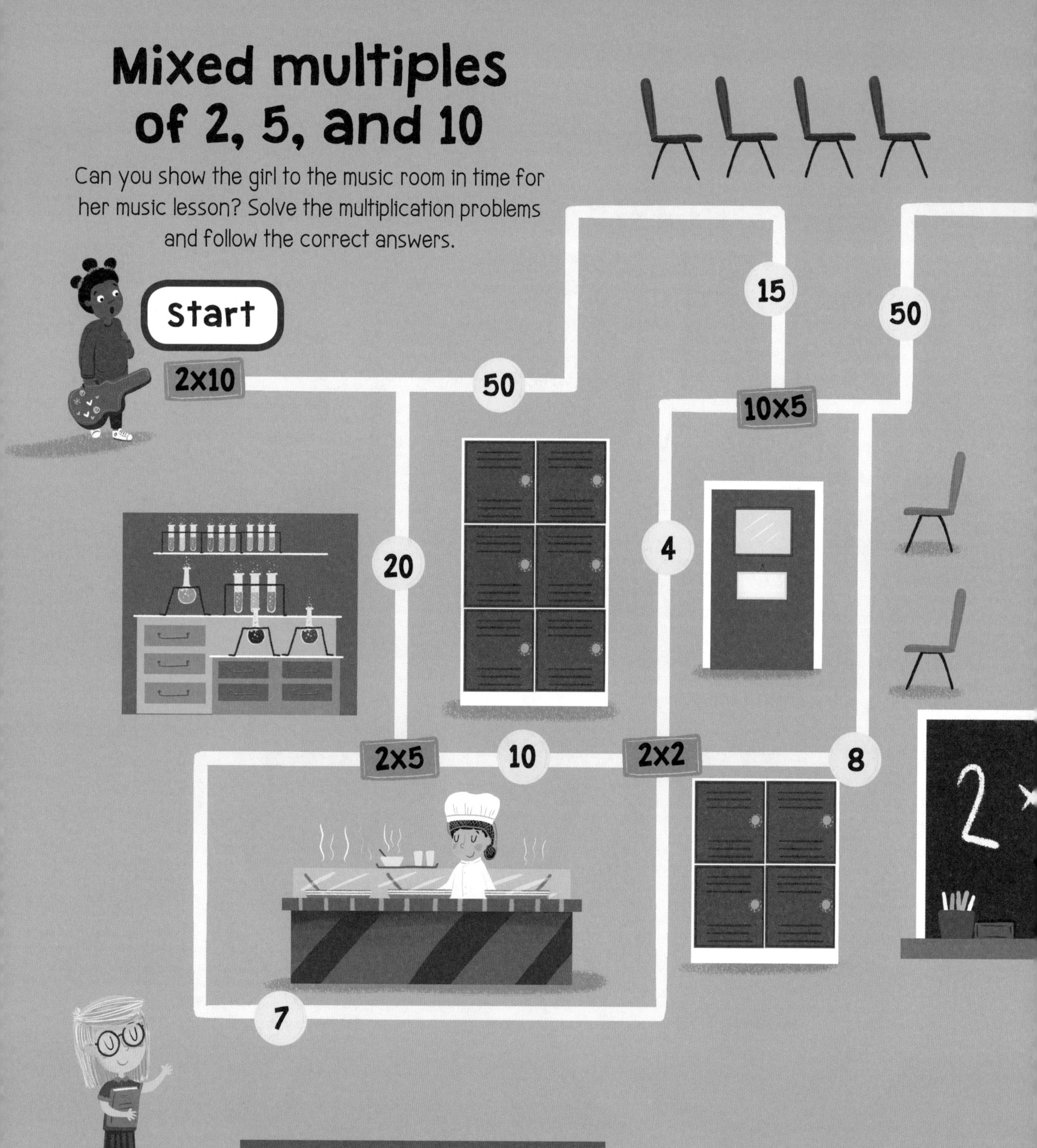

10x2
10
50
5x10
15
10x6
20
10x10
30
35
60
66
5x6
100
25
50
20
5x5
Finish

Multiples of 4

Help the elephant navigate around the zoo to find the waterfall enclosure. Solve the multiplication problems and follow the route with the correct answers.

Top Tip

Multiplying by 4 is the same as doubling and doubling again:
(7 + 7) + (7 + 7) = 28

21
4x3
12
20
4x2
18
8
4x5
10
44
4x11
48
Finish
16
15
4x10
24
14
40
30
4x6

Multiples of 8

Answer the calculations and follow the trail with the correct answers to help the dinosaur find her eggs before the volcano erupts!

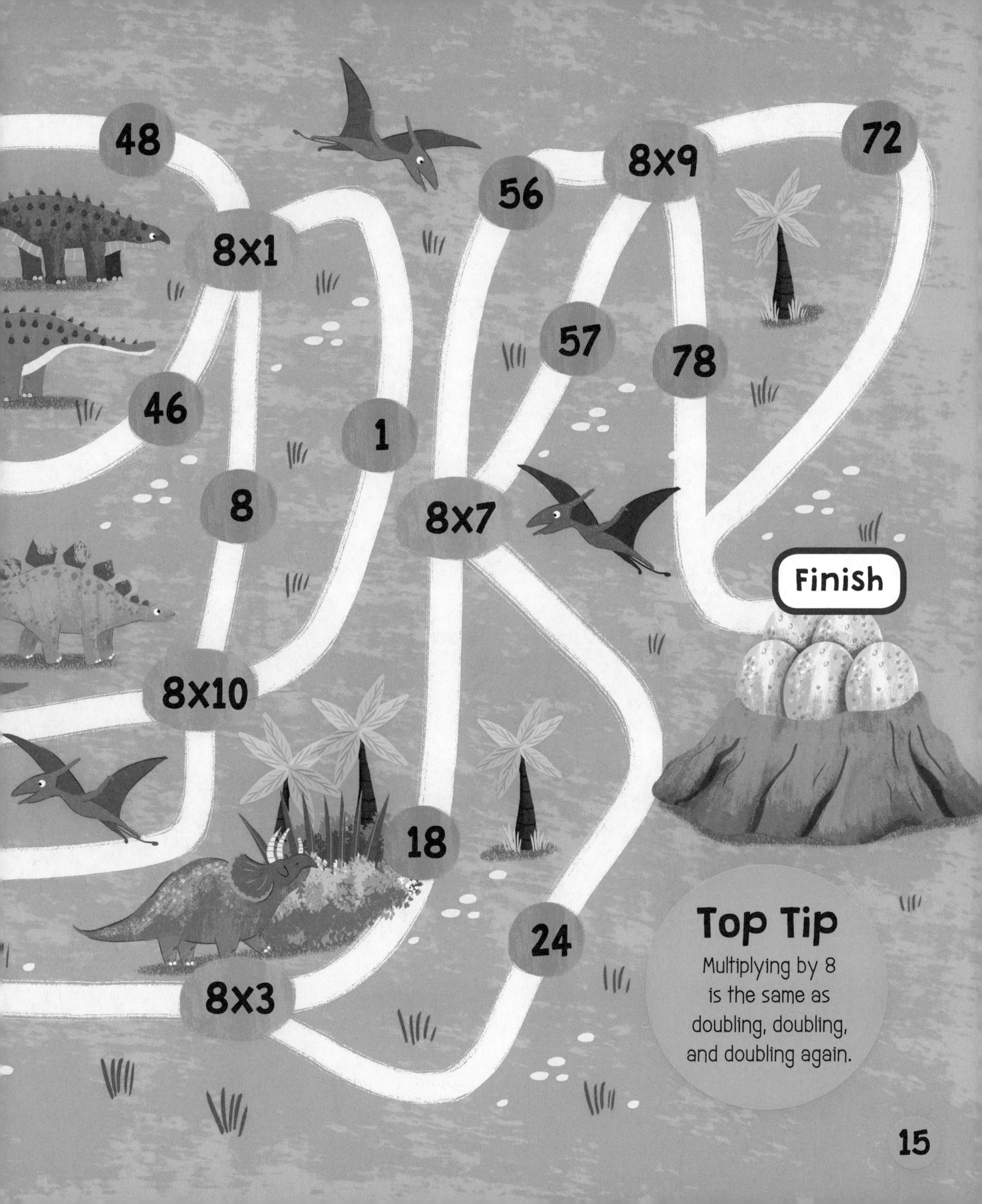

Top Tip

Multiplying by 8 is the same as doubling, doubling, and doubling again.

Mixed multiples of 2, 4, and 8

Speed through the number problems and follow the correct answers to get the family to the airport in time!

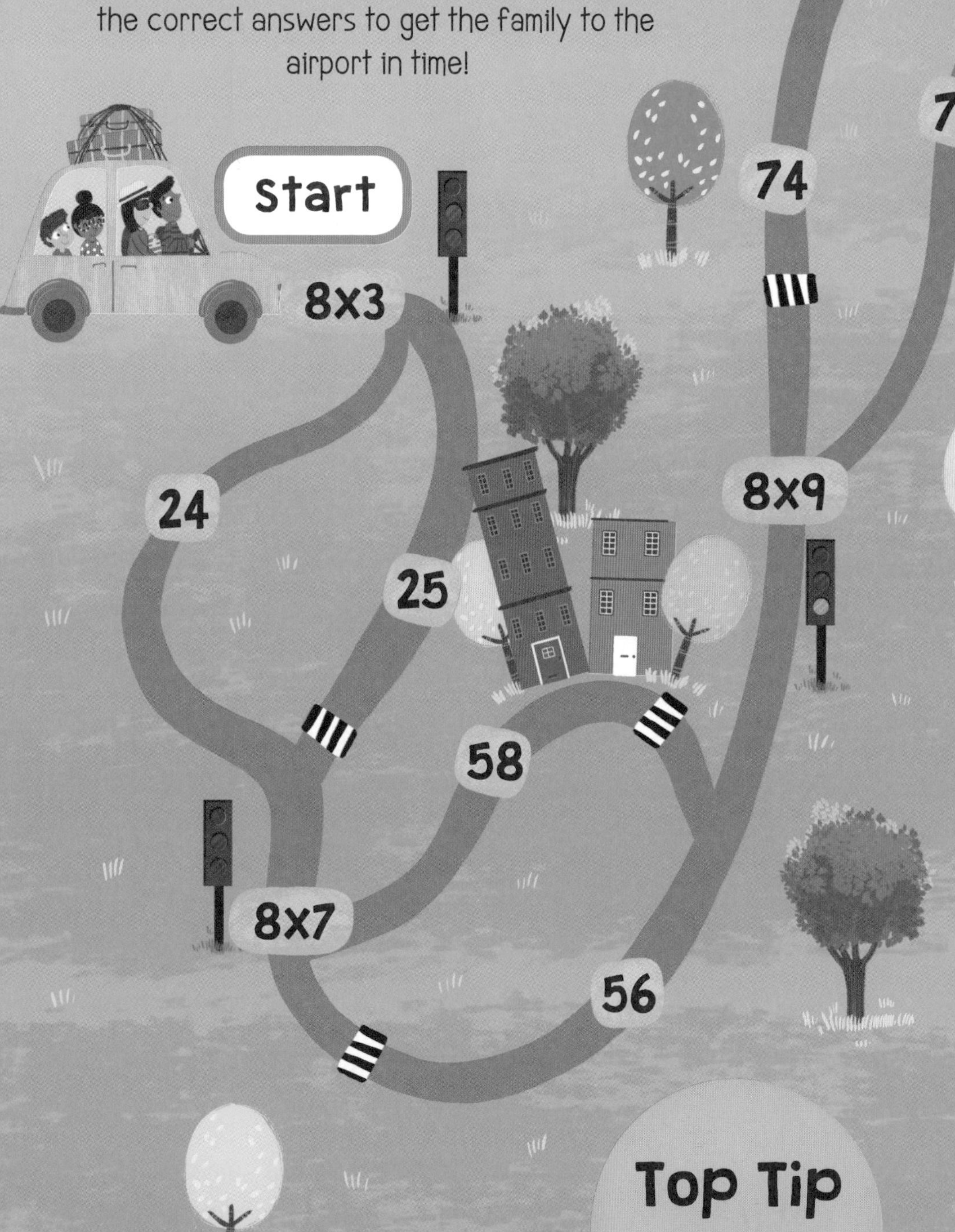

Top Tip

Count in 2s, 4s, and 8s.

2x3
4x9
6
8
34
16
36
18
2x11
4x7
2x9
28
22
21
24
24
20
2x10
Finish

Multiples of 3

Solve the calculations and follow the way with the correct answers to help the rocket land on the moon.

Start

3x4

13

12

3x3

9

10

3x8

24

11

3x5

8

15

3x11

14

33

3x12

Top Tip

Remember that
3 x 4 =
3 + 3 + 3 + 3

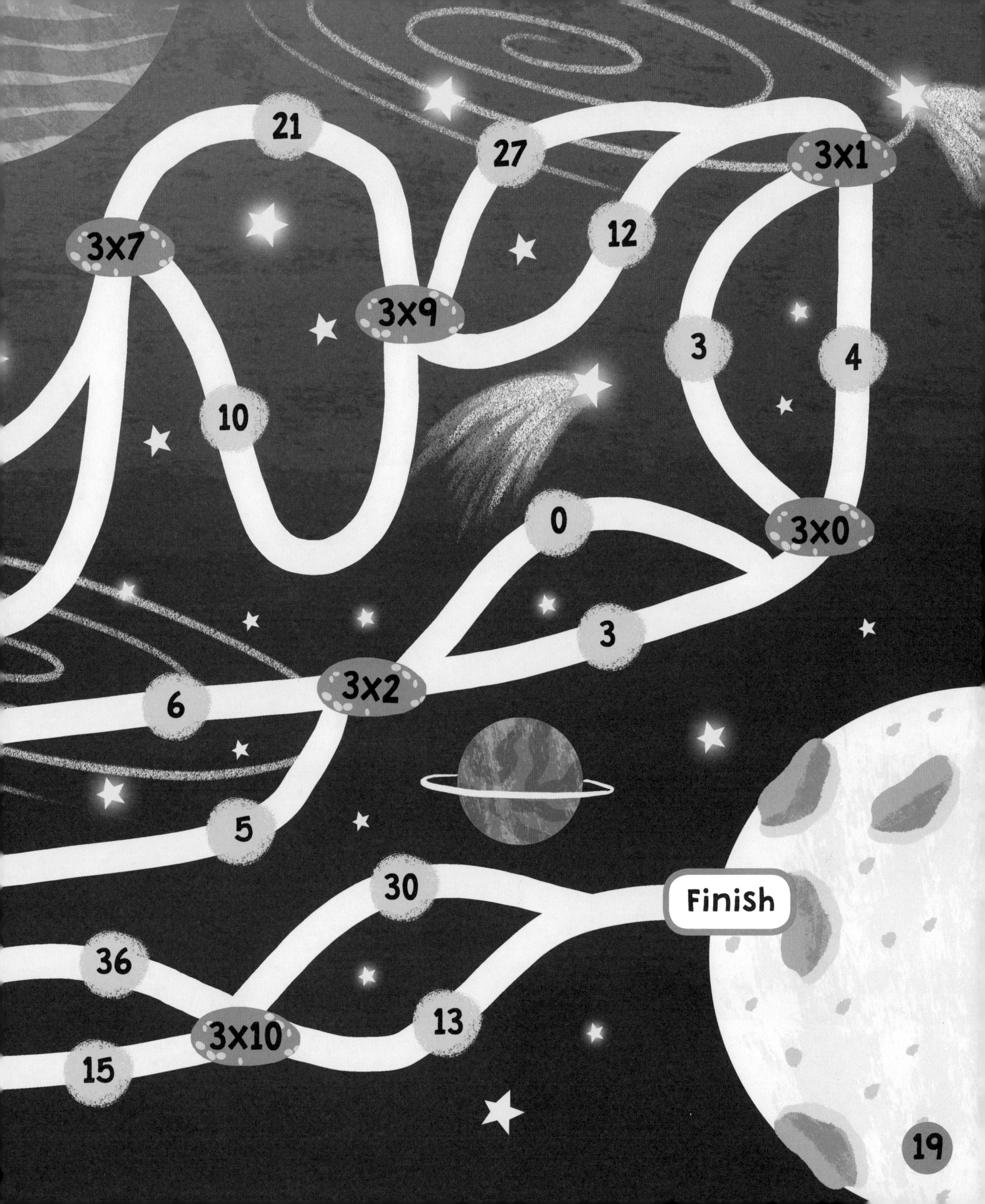
21
27
3x1
3x7
12
3x9
3
4
10
0
3x0
3
3x2
6
5
30
Finish
36
13
3x10
15

Multiples of 6

Help the boy find the bouncy castle at the funfair. Solve the multiplication problems and follow the path with the correct answers.

Top Tip

If you multiply 6 by an even number, the answer will end with the same digit as that number.

URGERS
6x8
Finish
42
48
6
7
6
0
35
6x6
6x1
6x10
6x0
36
66
60
6x11
66
ICE CREAM
CARS
16

Multiples of 9

Follow the numbers that are multiples of 9 to lead the scientist to the exit: it's time for a lunch break.

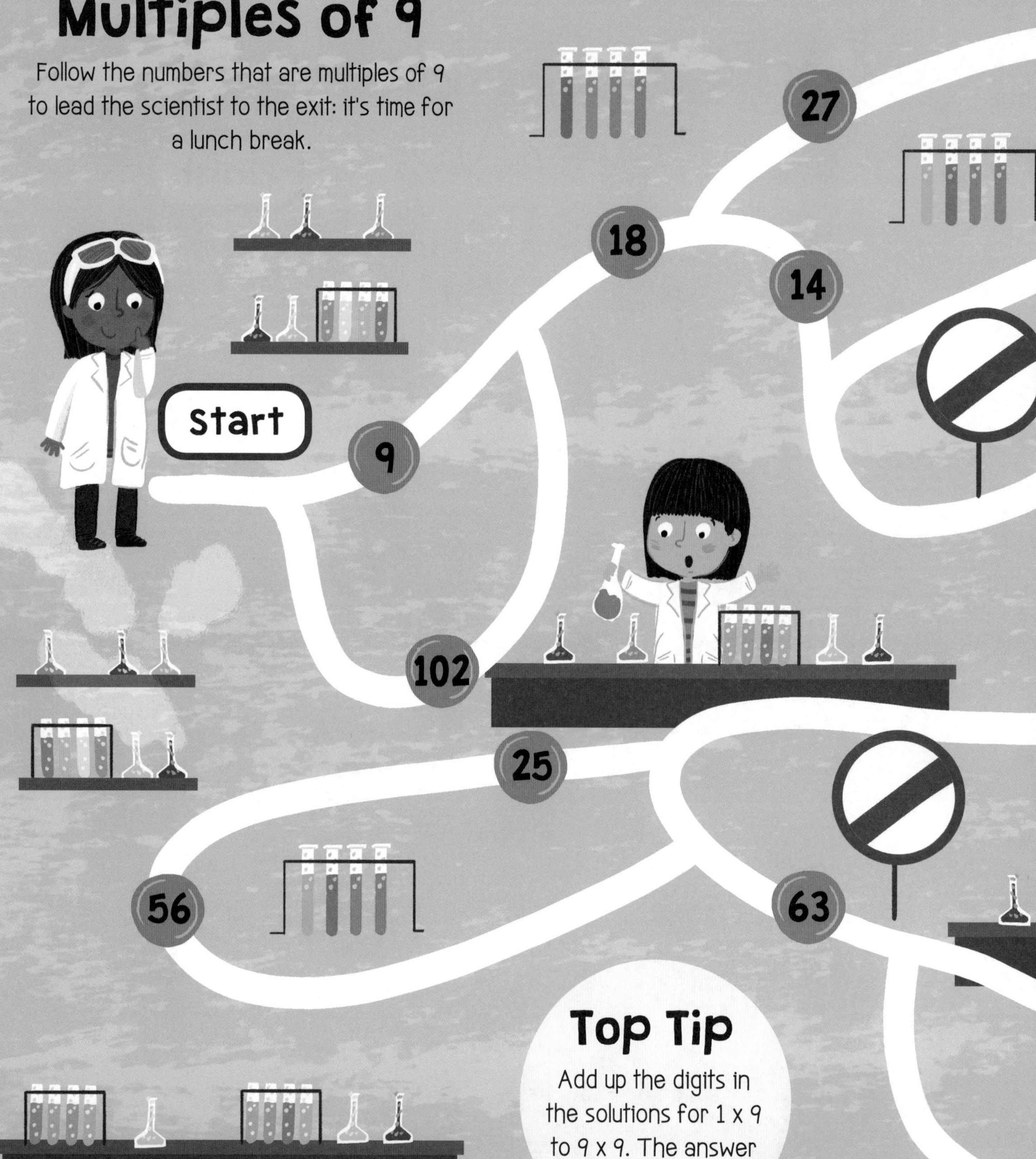

Top Tip

Add up the digits in the solutions for 1 x 9 to 9 x 9. The answer is always 9!

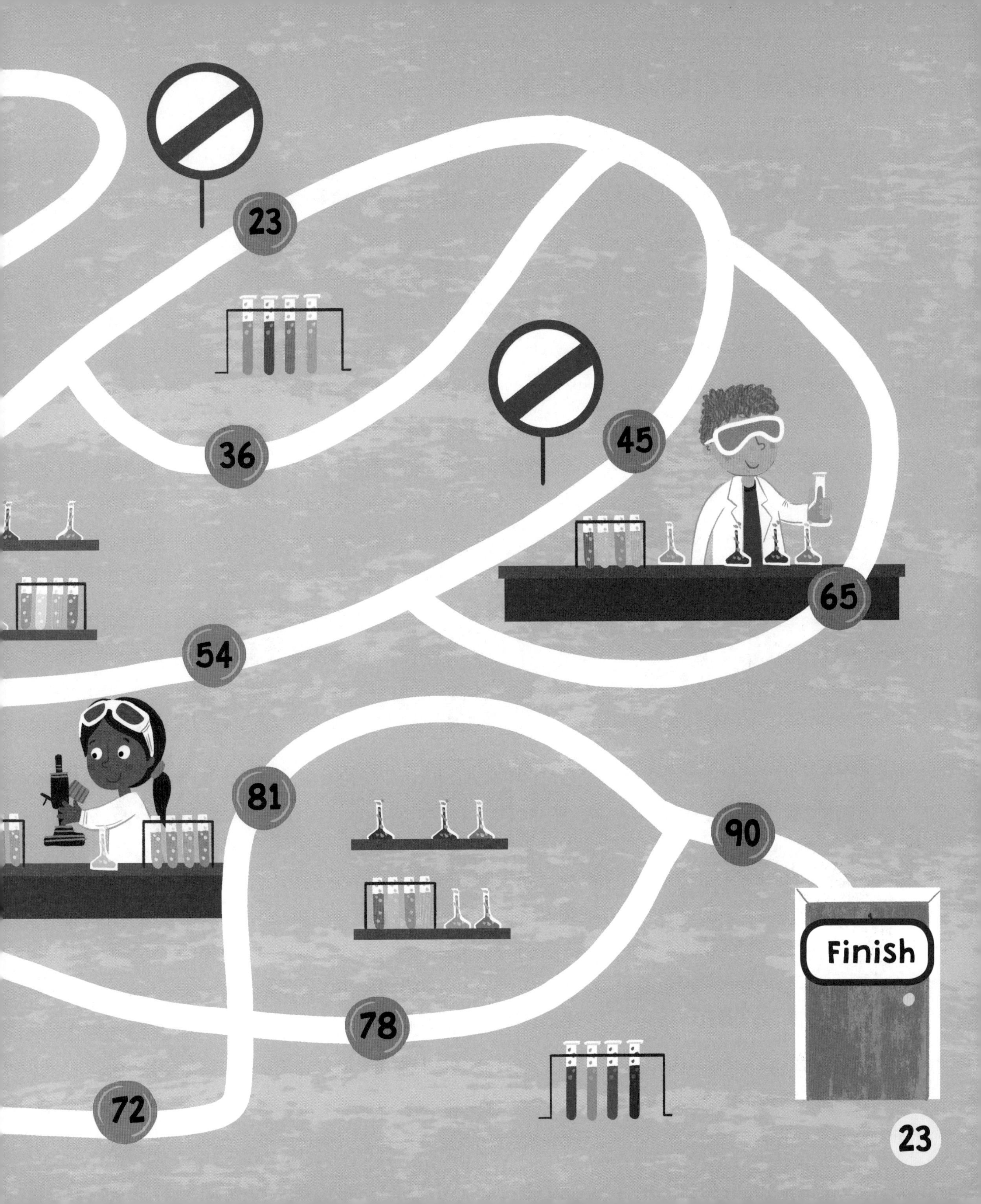
23
36
45
65
54
81
90
Finish
78
72

Mixed multiples of 3, 6, and 9

Help the pirate find the treasure. Solve the calculations and follow the correct answers.

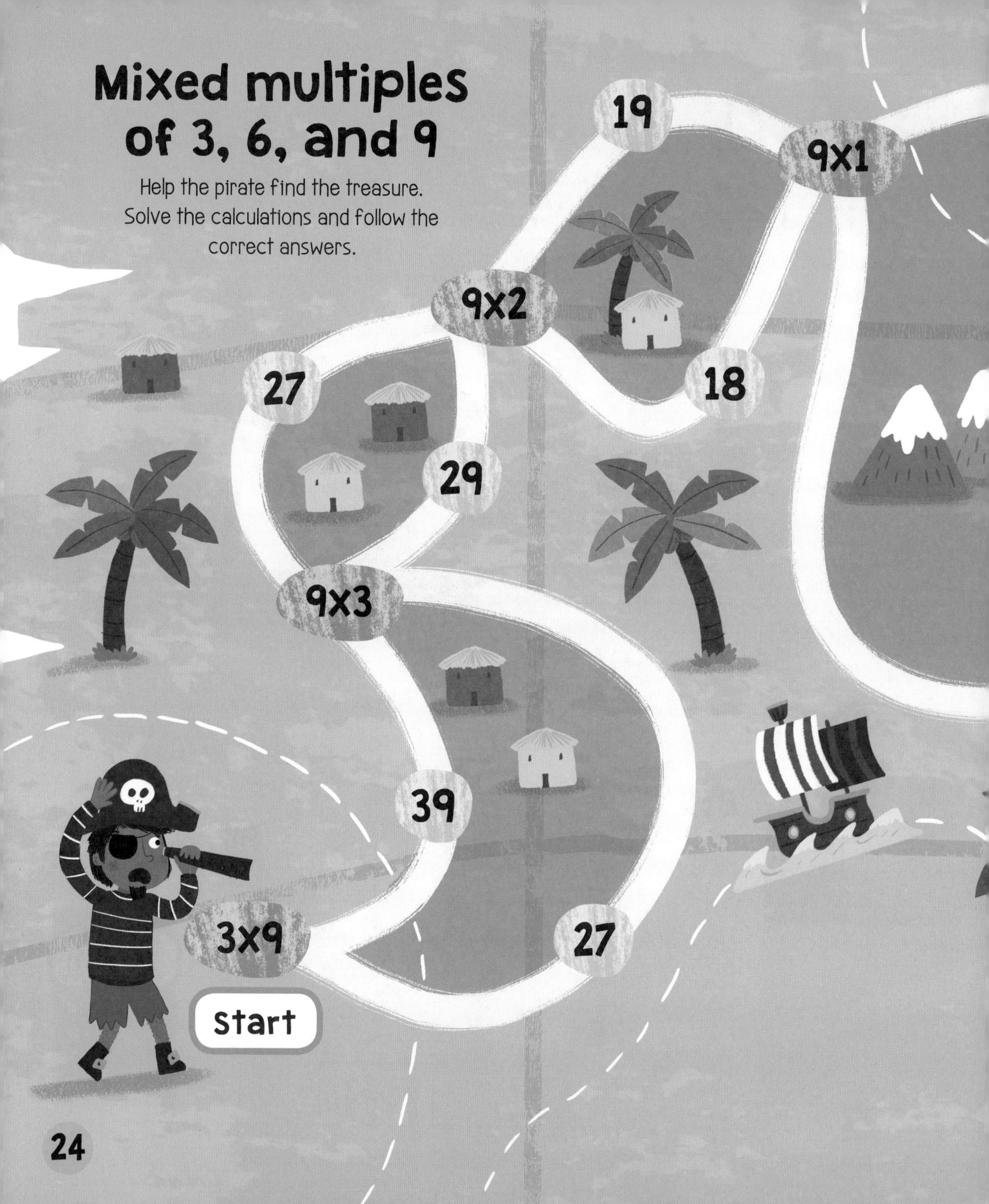

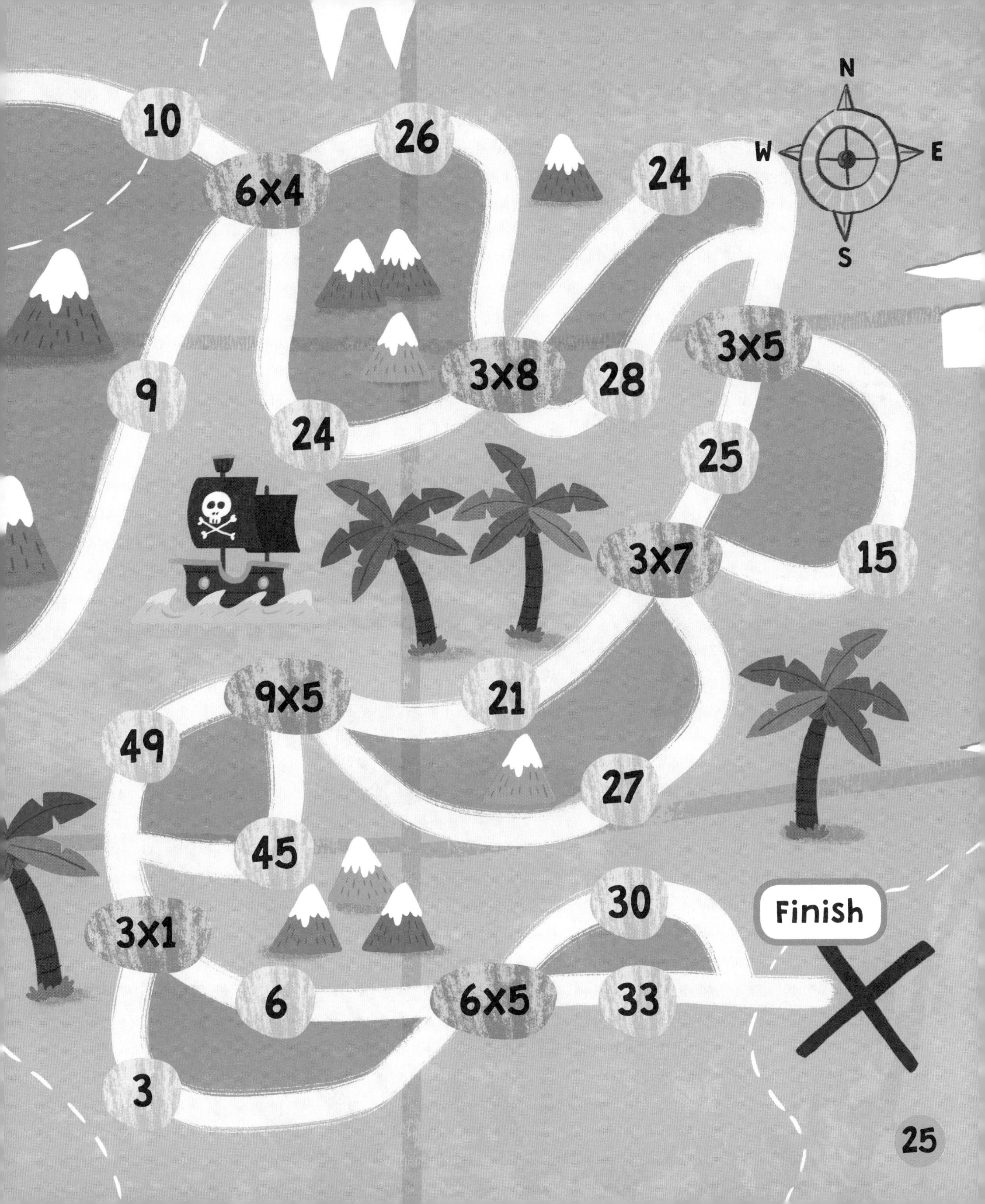
N
W
E
S
10
26
6x4
24
9
3x8
28
3x5
24
25
3x7
15
9x5
21
49
27
45
30
Finish
3x1
6
6x5
33
3

Multiples of 100

The girl has dropped her fishing net: follow the numbers that are multiples of 100 to help her find it.

Top Tip

Try counting in 100s.

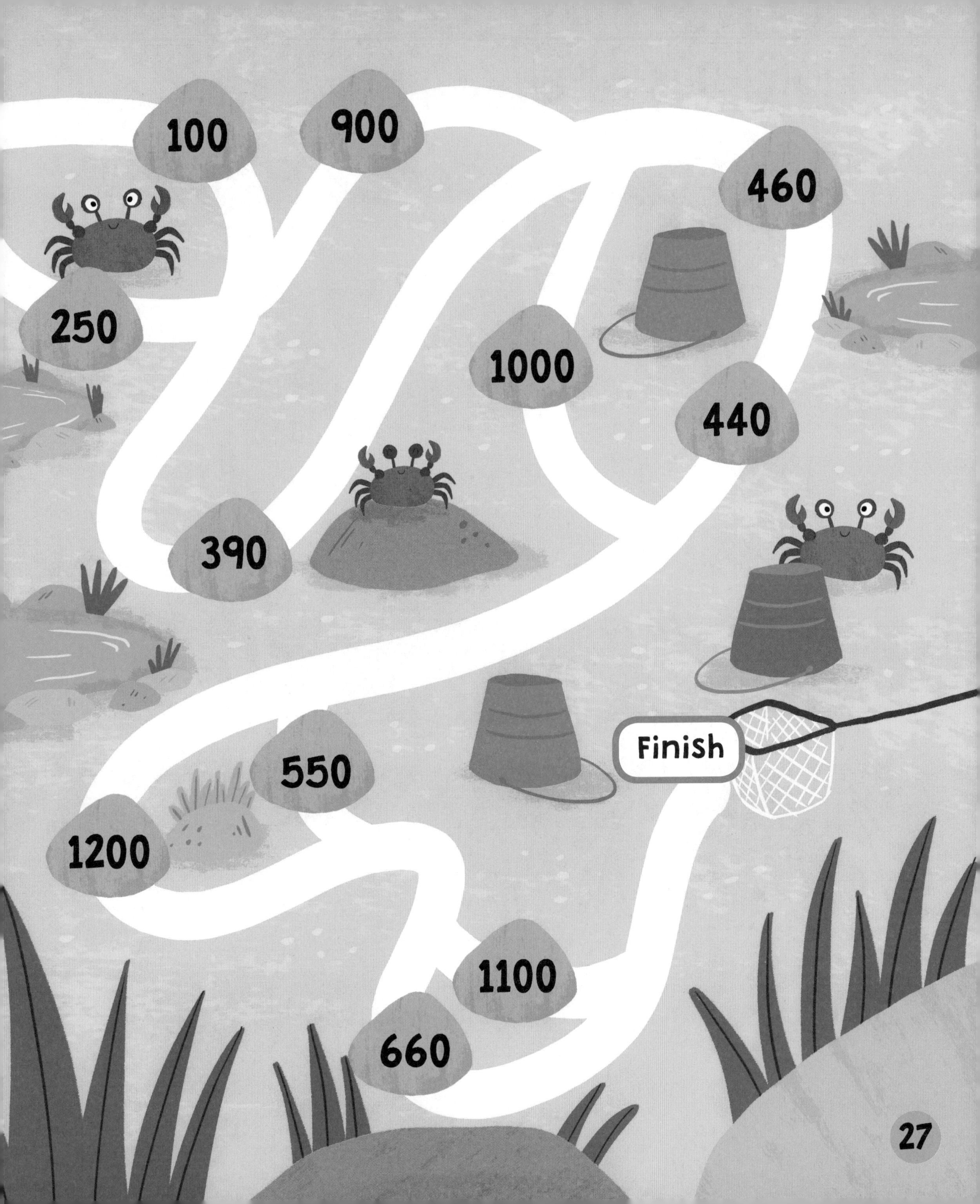
100
900
460
250
1000
440
390
Finish
550
1200
1100
660

Multiples of 50

Follow the numbers that are multiples of 50 to help the fly escape the spiders' web.

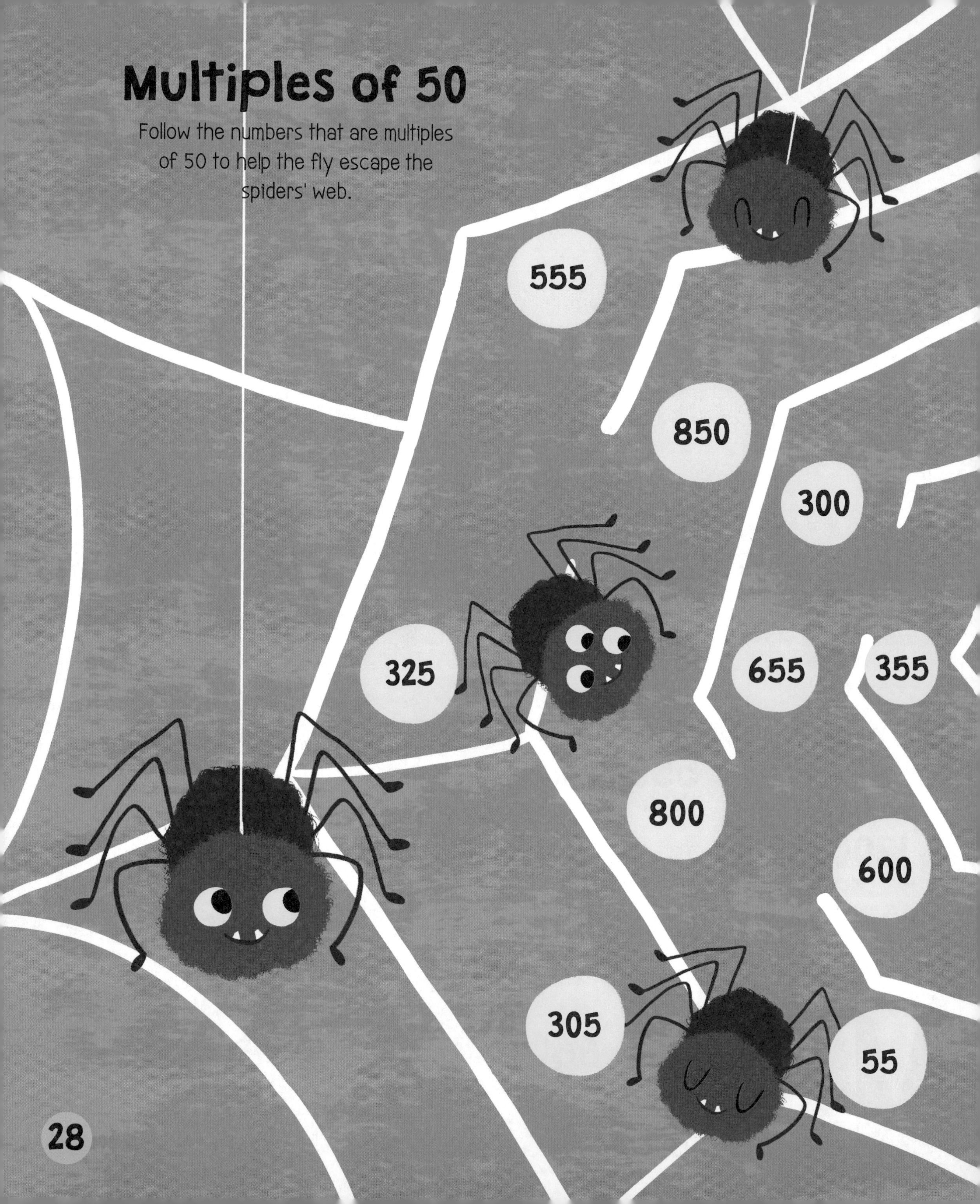

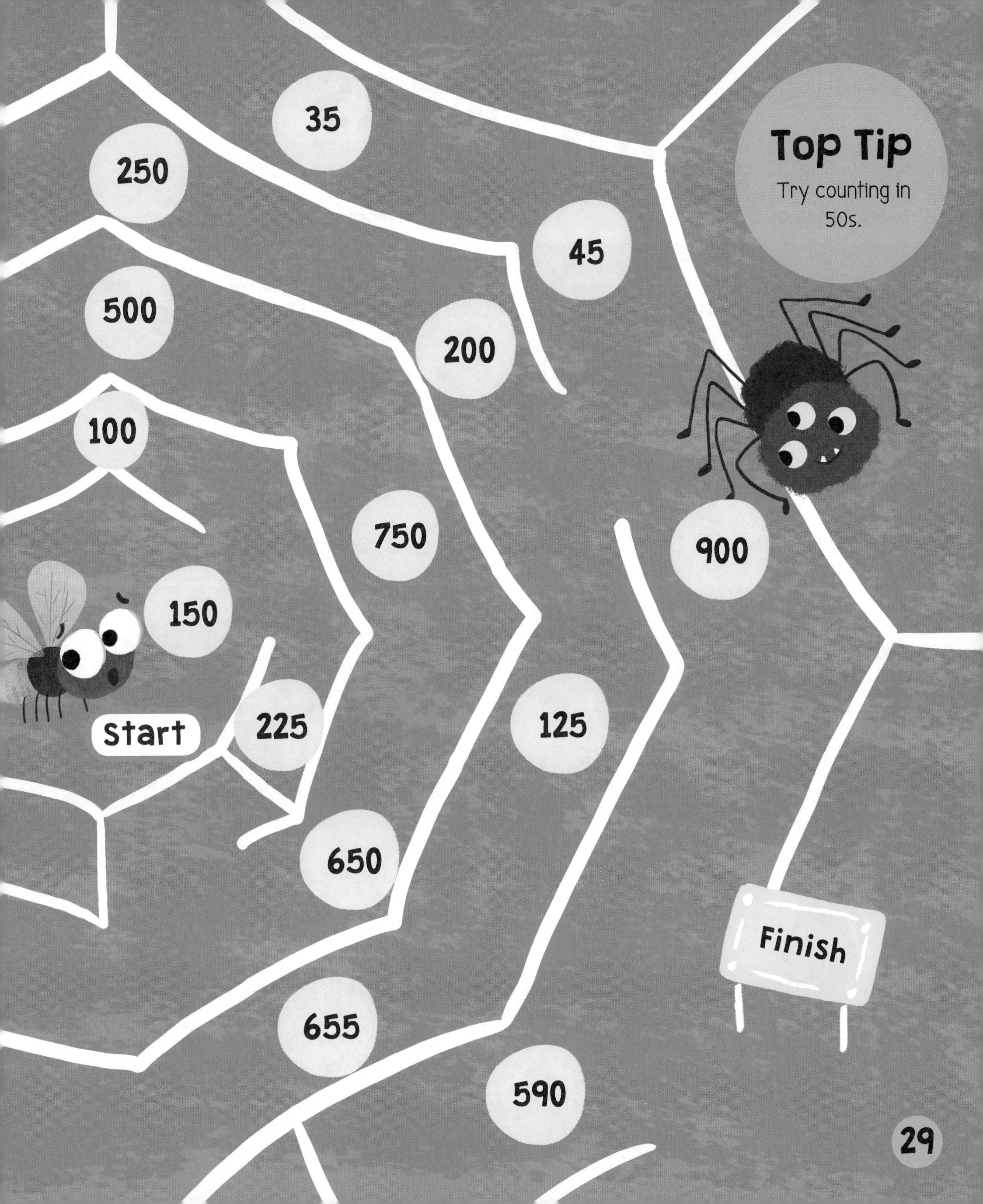

Top Tip

Try counting in 50s.

ANSWERS

4–5 Multiples of 2

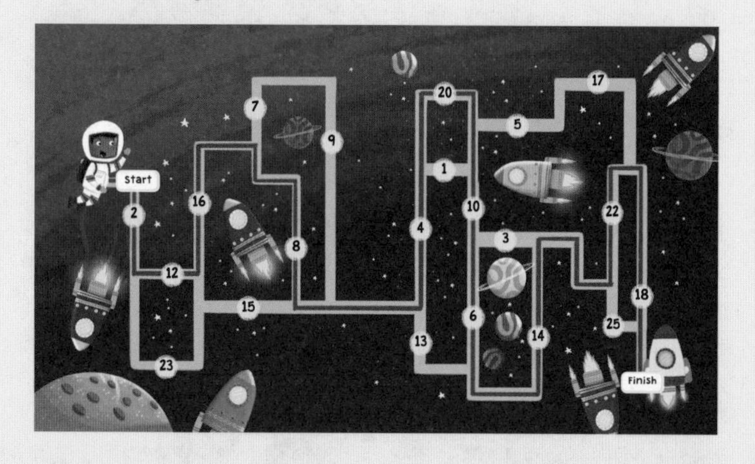

6–7 Multiples of 10

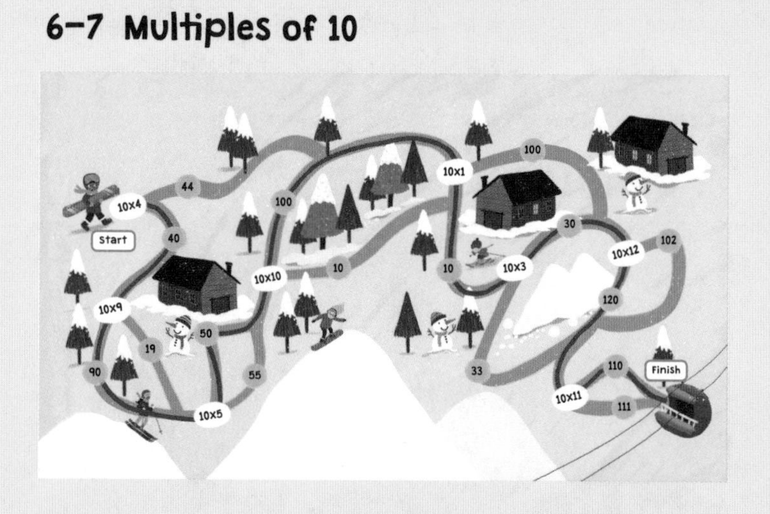

8–9 Multiples of 5

10–11 Mixed multiples of 2, 5, and 10

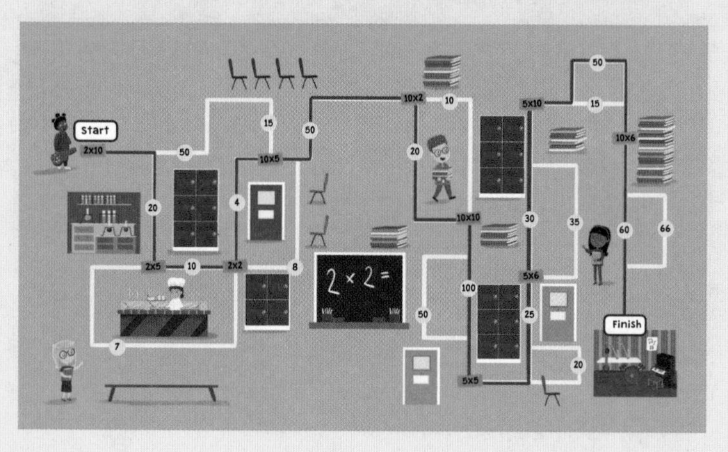

12–13 Multiples of 4

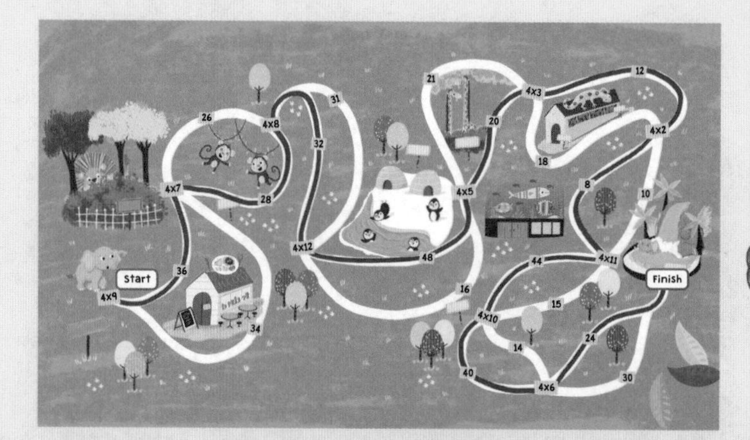

14–15 Multiples of 8

16–17 Mixed multiples of 2, 4, and 8

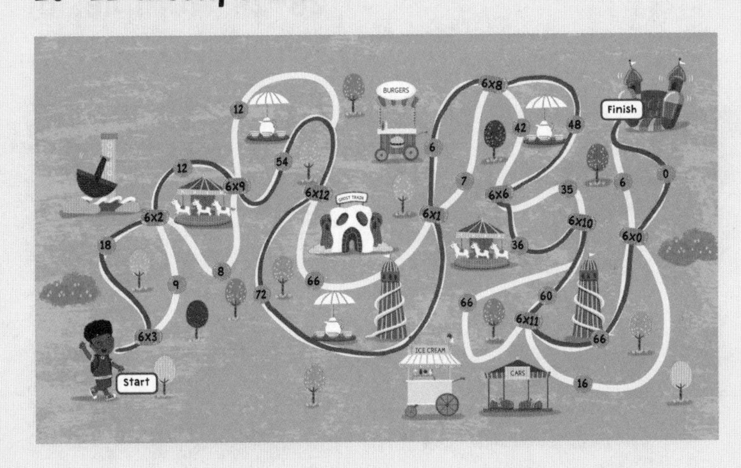

18–19 Multiples of 3

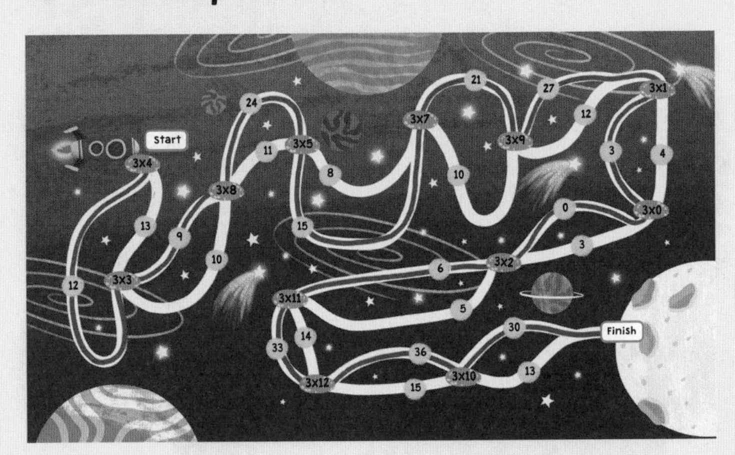

20–21 Multiples of 6

22–23 Multiples of 9

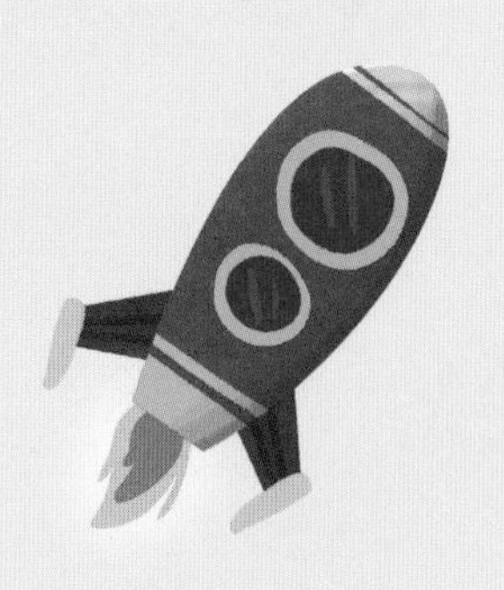

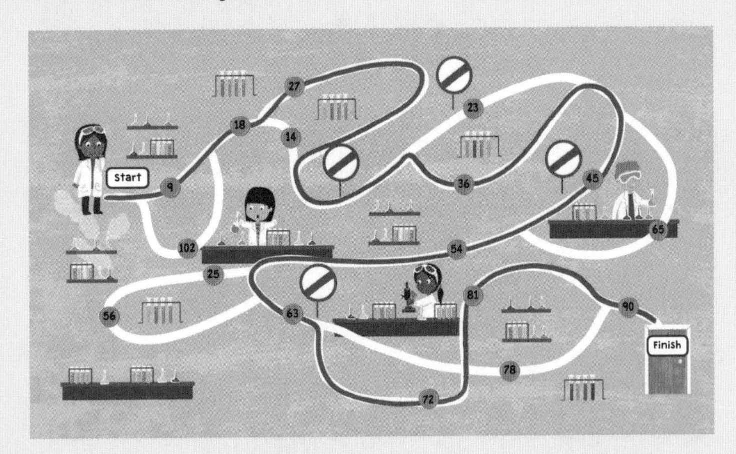

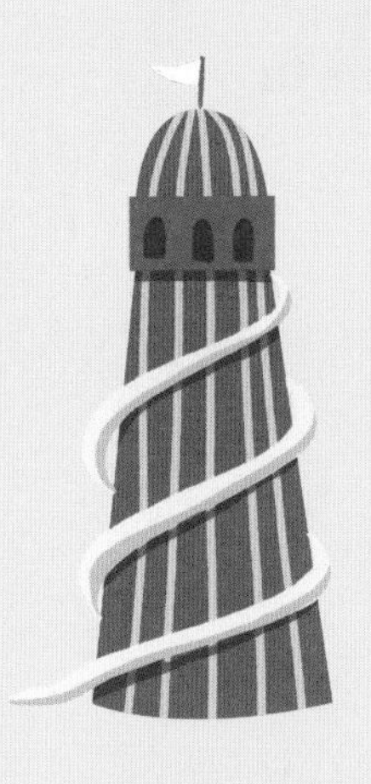

24–25 Mixed multiples of 3, 6, and 9

26–27 Multiples of 100

28–29 Multiples of 50

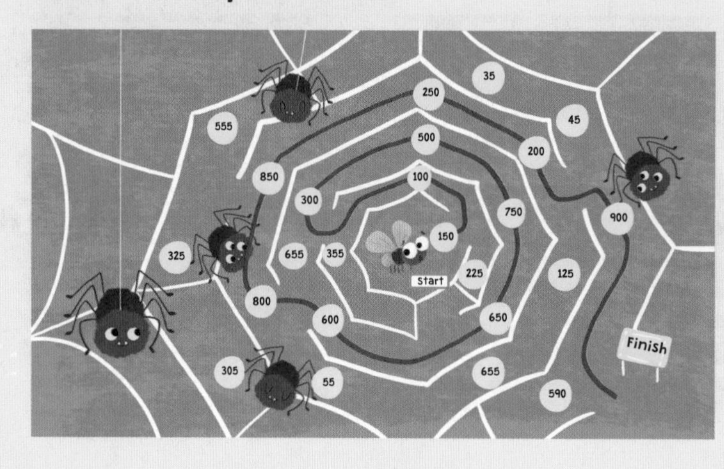